study guide

LOVELIFE

MARK DRISCOLL | song of solomon

Published 2010
by

www.gotothehub.com

3405 Milton Avenue, Suite 207
Dallas, TX 75205

Printed in the United States

BIBLE STUDIES

BUY.RENT.DOWNLOAD

DANIEL

Daniel, Things to Come
Bible Study Series by Tommy Nelson
4 DVD Curriculum
Companion Study Guide
Understand prophecy and how it can change your life today

ECCLESIASTES

A Life Well Lived (A Study of Ecclesiastes)
Bible Study Series by Tommy Nelson
4 DVD Curriculum
Companion Study Guide
A Life Well Lived paperback book

ROMANS

NEW! Romans, The Letter that Changed the World, Vol. I and II
Bible Study Series by Tommy Nelson
DVD Curriculum
Companion Study Guide
Packages and bulk discounts available

PHILIPPIANS

NEW! Philippians, To Live is Christ & to Die is Gain
Bible Study Series by Matt Chandler
4 DVD Curriculum
Companion Study Guide
Packages and bulk discounts available

VINTAGE JESUS

NEW! Vintage Jesus, Timeless Answers to Timely Questions
Bible Study Series by Mark Driscoll
4 DVD Curriculum
Companion Study Guide
Packages and bulk discounts available

SONG OF SOLOMON

Song of Solomon for Students
DVD Curriculum by Tommy Nelson
Designed for Students grades 7th thru 12th
Perfect for Students, Student Leaders and Parents

aCKNOWLedgeMeNTS

The Hub wishes to thank the following friends, without whose help, this series and study guide would not have been possible:

Jim Gribnitz, Crosswise Media (Study Guide Consultant and Behind the Book) • Matt Coleman, Unblind Productions, Producer • Drew Rogers, Livingstone Designs • Shatrine Krake, Krake Designs • Sue Ann Reynolds, Round Tu-it Office Support • Laura Davenport - Jason Countryman, PocketPak Albums • James River Assembly, www.jamesriver.org - John Lindell, Pastor of James River Assembly - Brad Wicks and entire Media Staff at James River

aBOUT The huB

Thanks for taking a moment to learn more about us. Our organization began in 1995 working with one speaker, Tommy Nelson and one amazing message, The Song of Solomon. It was and is our privilege to help champion God's written Word on Love, Dating, Marriage and Sex based directly on Song of Solomon. It is a book that has been censored for centuries and it has been a total blessing and thrill to see it change my life, and millions of others.

As of August 2009 we have rebranded our organization to reflect the root of our passion and the future of our organization:

To Develop, Find and Share life changing Bible Centric tools that move people forward. We have renamed our organization to The Hub. It is our passion and commitment to be a Hub for unique, challenging and grace filled resources. I hope you will agree after you participate and interact with one of our resources. God Bless you and know that if you will listen, God's Truth will move you forward in life, no matter where you have been or are currently.

Doug Hudson, *President - The Hub*

TABLE of CONTENTS

	PAGE
BIBLE STUDIES	iii
ACKNOWLEDGEMENTS/ABOUT THE HUB	iv
STUDY TIPS	vii
ABOUT THE AUTHOR	x

SESSION ONE — 1
sex: god, gross, or gift?

SESSION TWO — 9
god's intentions in marriage and the freedom that follows

SESSION THREE — 17
discovering oasis

SESSION FOUR — 27
foxes in the vineyard

SESSION FIVE — 35
the wedding and the last day

SESSION SIX — 45
sin's damaging effects

SESSION SEVEN — 53
the fight

SESSION EIGHT — 63
servant lovers

SESSION NINE — 71
visual and verbal generosity

SESSION TEN — 81
question and answer

BEHIND THE BOOK SONG OF SOLOMON	87
BIBLIOGRAPHY	95
APPENDIX	97
ICE BREAKERS	99

THE NEXT LEVEL OF BIBLE STUDY

SIMPLE TRUTH	AMAZING TEACHERS	EASY ACCESS
PHILIPPIANS	MARK DRISCOLL	→ BUY
ROMANS	MATT CHANDLER	→ RENT
ECCLESSIASTES	TOMMY NELSON	→ DOWNLOAD
DANIEL		
SONG OF SOLOMON		
VINTAGE JESUS		

WWW.GOTOTHEHUB.COM

ACCESS THE TRUTH ANYTIME, ANYWHERE!

sTudy Tips

BEFORE YOU GO ANY FURTHER...READ THIS!

If you are a small group leader, thanks for taking the opportunity to shepherd others along the way. And if you are using this series for personal study, get ready for a life-changing experience you will want to share with others! Here are a few tips as you get started with the series:

- This study was designed with small groups in mind. So put a small group together and get started.
- The series is also perfect for individuals or couples who are looking for ways to deepen their devotions or find practical ways to apply the timeless truths of Scripture.
- Song of Solomon is designed to be used as either a 10-week or a 5-week study.
- Depending on the length of your meeting time, you can watch two sessions per meeting to make Song of Solomon a 5-week series.

A WORD TO SMALL GROUP LEADERS

Special Note - take a moment to go to Behind The Book feature. This is a quick overview that will give you the who, what, when, where and why of Song of Solomon. There is no separate leader's guide. Leaders are facilitators of the material: Answers to Text Questions are in the back of the study guide.

Effective small group interactions can maximize the impact of any teaching. We remember what we *discuss* and *discover* much better than what we merely hear. This is your privilege as a leader. Help them in the process of discovery. Remember that your group is to facilitate discussion, not lecture. They have just heard a 30-minute sermon—they do not need another one. You are a facilitator of discussion, not a preacher.

FEELINGS

Be sensitive to the fact that sex and marriage in general can be a painful topic for many people.

- We tend to relax around food, whether dessert or a potluck supper. Many groups choose to rotate the responsibility for snacks.

...continued on next page

- Lay ground rules. It should help to reassure folks that your group will be "safe".
- Do not require anyone to share—even questions that don't seem threatening to you may feel so to others.
- Model openness and honesty. If others seem hesitant to share, show them how it's done.
- Be considerate of singles. This study is aimed at married and engaged couples, and the questions in this packet reflect that. If your group includes single people, modify the questions to include them.

FORMAT
Each session's guide will follow a consistent pattern.

- Icebreaker—for each session we've included a question or activity intended to help folks get to know each other in a lighthearted way. We have suggested "breaking the ice" before turning on the TV.
- DVD—the video teaching portion of each session lasts between 25 and 40 minutes.
- Discussion Questions—the questions are designed to move people toward discussing what they will do about what they've heard. However, they do not ask for inappropriate detail in a group setting.
- Application—this is the occasion for making a personal commitment to act. Since some application points could be embarrassing, sharing them with the group is optional.
- Homework—group members are urged to follow through on their personal applications. Also, they are reminded to discuss with their spouses the more intimate questions suggested by the DVD. You may choose to print out the Application and Homework questions for your group members each week.
- Consider closing your time by praying for the pastoral staff of your church or any other spiritual leaders in your community. It would be a blessing to let that leader know he and his wife are being prayed for regularly, specifically with regards to their marriage.

FACILITATION
For many it helps to think of themselves as facilitators (those who help things go smoothly) rather than leaders. Planning ahead will help tremendously.

- Budget your time—Though it is not imperative for you to review the material ahead of time, it would probably be helpful to watch the DVD and review the questions before your group meets. Consider how long you will meet, how long the DVD session is, and calculate how long you can spend on each of the questions and other agenda items.

- Prioritize your questions—If you can't discuss all the questions (some sessions have more suggested questions than others) identify the ones you want to be sure and cover. If you want to combine or rephrase questions, feel free, but be sure to keep discussions practical rather than theoretical.
- Be yourself—relax. Get to know your group, and allow them to get to know you. You don't have to know all the answers or have it all together. You and your group are learning together and encouraging each other along your spiritual path.

BEFORE EACH SESSION WE ENCOURAGE LEADERS TO:

- Pray—ask the Lord for guidance on how to lead the members in your group. Pray that He will show you ways to stimulate genuine, dynamic and open communication.

- Preview—it will be very beneficial for you to watch the session before you share it with your group. You will notice the key points from each session and you can better facilitate the discussion questions within your group.

- Prepare—a small group will only go as deep and be as transparent as the leader. If a leader or facilitator is not willing to get personal, then the group will float on the surface. Let God speak through your own struggles and weaknesses.

May God bless your study!

ABOUT The auThor

Pastor Mark Driscoll founded Mars Hill Church *(www.marshillchurch.org)* in Seattle in the fall of 1996. The church has grown from a small Bible study to over six thousand people in one of America's least churched cities. He co-founded and is president of the Acts 29 Church Planting Network *(www.acts29network.org)*, which has planted over one hundred churches in the U.S. and internationally. Most recently he founded the Resurgence Missional Theology Co-operative *(www.theresurgence.com)*.

His writing includes the books *Vintage Church, Vintage Jesus, Death by Love, Religion Saves, The Radical Reformission: Reaching Out Without Selling Out* and *Confessions of a Reformission Rev.: Hard Lessons from an Emerging Missional Church*. He also contributed to the books *The Supremacy of Christ in a Postmodern World*, edited by John Piper and Justin Taylor, and *Listening to the Beliefs of Emerging Churches*, edited by Robert Webber.

Media coverage of Pastor Mark varies just as widely, including such outlets as National Public Radio, The Bible Answer Man, Mother Jones magazine, the Associated Press, USA Today, the New York Times, Blender music magazine, Outreach magazine, Preaching Today, Leadership magazine, and ABC Television.

Most enjoyably, Pastor Mark and his high school sweetheart, Grace, delight in raising their three sons and two daughters, playing baseball with the boys and accompanying the girls on "daddy dates."

LOVELIFE

SESSION ONE | SEX: GOD, GROSS, OR GIFT?

GENESIS 2:18-25

I like loud things.

I love going to sporting events, concerts, and a bunch of other gatherings that are just plain loud. In venues like that, I generally start out trying to have conversations with my friends and family that I am with, but then as the night goes on, I find myself having to scream in order to have any communication whatsoever with them. I usually start to sit back and become simply an observer, totally taking in the experience instead of adding my voice.

It often seems pointless to fight the noise.

This is a lot like sexuality in our culture. The media screams messages about sexuality in our culture. They portray sexuality however they feel like, as if they invented it and therefore have the right to do so. Christians initially stood up and denounced these messages that paraded sexuality around loosely, peddling the gift of God for profit. Eventually though, the force has become too strong. The volume of sex in the media has permeated our culture, and Christians have let the world become their concert. The temptation to shut our mouths, sit back and listen has overtaken us.

After all, what do we know for sure about sex? Maybe consensus and popular culture/opinion is right? It seems like literally everyone and everything says sexuality is something for each person to just enjoy however and whenever they feel like it. Is that so bad?

Maybe it is old-fashioned to view sex as something that needs to be reserved for only the marital relationship? It is old for sure. (See the Book of Genesis.)

I know it is loud out there. I hear it too. Let's sit back, relax, quiet our minds, and listen to the only voice on the matter that really matters—God's. He has the ultimate authority to say what sex is and is not.

Open up to Genesis, and let's ignore the noise.

the word

18Then the LORD God said, "It is not good that the man should be alone; I will make him a helper fit for him." 19Now out of the ground the LORD God had formed every beast of the field and every bird of the heavens and brought them to the man to see what he would call them. And whatever the man called every living creature, that was its name. 20The man gave names to all livestock and to the birds of the heavens and to every beast of the field. But for Adam there was not found a helper fit for him. 21So the LORD God caused a deep sleep to fall upon the man, and while he slept took one of his ribs and closed up its place with flesh. 22And the rib that the LORD God had taken from the man he made into a woman and brought her to the man. 23Then the man said, "This at last is bone of my bones and flesh of my flesh; she shall be called Woman, because she was taken out of Man." 24Therefore a man shall leave his father and his mother and hold fast to his wife, and they shall become one flesh. 25And the man and his wife were both naked and were not ashamed.

DISCUSSION QUESTIONS

1. What are the six biblical reasons given for having sex?

    1. _____

    2. _____

    3. _____

    4. _____

    5. _____

    6. _____

2. What does it mean to view sex as our "god"? What are some ways you see this manifest itself in your workplace, on TV, in the movies?

_____

_____

_____

_____

> THE MOST BEAUTIFUL, PLEASURABLE, AMAZING THING THAT GOD MADE WAS THE HUMAN BODY.

3. If sex is "gross" to someone, how will they demonstrate that? What will the external evidences of that mindset be?

_____

_____

_____

_____

4. What are the consequences of each of these first two views?

_____
_____
_____
_____

5. Which of these two views, if either, have you held in the past? Did your upbringing lend itself to either view?

_____
_____
_____
_____

6. Explain the view of sex as a gift. What are the implications of viewing sex as a gift? Specifically, how does such a view affect attitudes and behavior?

_____
_____
_____
_____

7. What, if anything, makes it hard for Christians to accept the view that sex is a gift from God?

_____
_____
_____
_____

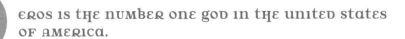
8. Of the six benefits of the gift of sex (pleasure, children, oneness, comfort, protection from temptation, and glorifying God) are there any that are difficult for you to accept or understand? Why?

_____

_____

_____

_____

9. Consider the progression into marriage described in Genesis. A man will:
    1. leave his father and mother (become independent of his parents)
    2. be united to his wife (get married)
    3. the two will become one flesh (have sex). What are the consequences of getting this progression out of order?

_____

_____

_____

_____

MEMORY VERSE

"Then the Lord God said, 'It is not good that the man should be alone; I will make him a helper fit for him.' " (Genesis 2:18, ESV)

application

Identify one specific action you will take as a result of this lesson. Write it down. If appropriate, share it with your small group.

_____

_____

_____

_____

homework

Follow through on your application point from the discussion time. Discuss this question with your spouse (or a close, *same-sex friend*, if you are single): Is there any acceptable marital pleasure or body part that is "gross" or "a god" for me? Ask God to renew your mind in this area.

PRAYER requests

_____

_____

_____

_____

_____

_____

_____

LOVELIFE

SESSION TWO | God's intentions in marriage and the freedom that follows

SONG OF SOLOMON 1:1-11

I would hate to be a woman in this culture.

Look at every magazine at every grocery store and gas station in America, and who is on it? It seems that every single one has an unbelievably gorgeous woman on the front that has been photographed in just the right way to accentuate every curve and airbrushed to hide every flaw. Look at every TV show on any network, day or night. The women are insanely beautiful and have designers that fight to get them the latest clothes, trainers that line up to work with them, and make-up professionals that spend an hour getting them ready to go on air. Movies? Video games? Advertisements on TV? Previews at the movies? On the web? They all say the same thing: the measure of beauty for women is off the charts.

It would stink to be a girl sometimes.

And what about men? The Bible calls men to the highest character, but the world sure seems to send a different message. The mass media lets us know that the measure of a man is how many women he gets in his bed and never feels obligated to call again. A 'real' man doesn't need anyone but himself. Women are an object to be used and abused to a 'real' man, according to the group-think of our day. This is completely counter to all biblical teaching, but it is the mindset that permeates our culture.

So what is the standard of beauty? What is true character?

If only God would speak on the issue…

Oh wait—He does.

the word

¹The Song of Songs, which is Solomon's. ²Let him kiss me with the kisses of his mouth! For your love is better than wine; ³your anointing oils are fragrant; your name is oil poured out; therefore virgins love you. ⁴Draw me after you; let us run. The king has brought me into his chambers. We will exult and rejoice in you; we will extol your love more than wine; rightly do they love you. ⁵I am very dark, but lovely, O daughters of Jerusalem, like the tents of Kedar, like the curtains of Solomon. ⁶Do not gaze at me because I am dark, because the sun has looked upon me. My mother's sons were angry with me; they made me keeper of the vineyards, but my own vineyard I have not kept! ⁷Tell me, you whom my soul loves, where you pasture your flock, where you make it lie down at noon; for why should I be like one who veils herself beside the flocks of your companions? ⁸If you do not know, O most beautiful among women, follow in the tracks of the flock, and pasture your young goats beside the shepherds' tents. ⁹I compare you, my love, to a mare among Pharaoh's chariots. ¹⁰Your cheeks are lovely with ornaments, your neck with strings of jewels. ¹¹We will make for you ornaments of gold, studded with silver.

DISCUSSION QUESTIONS

1. Describe the cultural standard of beauty. How has this standard changed over time? What do all cultural standards have in common? How is it different for men and women in our culture?

_____

_____

_____

_____

2. What is meant by the statement, "Your standard of beauty is your spouse"? How can we cultivate this mindset of finding beauty in our spouse, regardless of the cultural standards around us?

_____

_____

_____

_____

> BE A STUDENT OF YOUR SPOUSE.

3. Why is it important for a man to consistently praise his wife's beauty?

_____

_____

_____

_____

4. How can the church edify and celebrate marriage?

_____

_____

_____

_____

THE STANDARD OF BEAUTY IS YOUR SPOUSE.

5. To what degree should the opinion of others matter with regard to a potential mate?

_____

_____

_____

_____

BE CAUTIOUS OF ANY RELATIONSHIP THAT CAUSES ANYONE TO BE SEPARATED FROM FELLOWSHIP.

6. What is good character? How can it be measured? Does anyone come to mind in particular when you think of someone of outstanding character?

_____

_____

_____

_____

8. Rather than nagging, how does the bride express her desire to be with her husband? Women, why is this approach difficult for many women? Men, what is attractive about it?

_____

_____

_____

_____

MEMORY VERSE

"Your name is oil poured out; therefore virgins love you."
(Song of Solomon 1:3b, ESV)

APPLICATION

Identify one specific action you will take as a result of this lesson. Write it down. If appropriate, share it with your small group.

_____

_____

_____

_____

DIVING DEEPER

A great memory verse for men: **Job 31:1**
"I have made a covenant with my eyes; how then could I gaze at a virgin?"

A great memory verse for women: **Proverbs 21:9** (or 25:24)
"It is better to live in a corner of the housetop than in a house shared with a quarrelsome wife."

homework

Follow through on your application point from the discussion time.

If married, discuss these questions as a couple:
- For men: Is there anything unattractive in my character?
- For women: How well do I pursue you?

If single, ask yourself:
- As I meet people, am I focused more on their character or on more superficial qualities? How can I be sure?
- What am I doing to cultivate godly character in myself?

PRAYER requests

_____

_____

_____

_____

_____

_____

_____

LOVELIFE

SESSION THREE | discovering oasis

SONG OF SOLOMON 1:12-2:16

Imagine for a moment that you are on a journey.

You have set out on a mission to 'find yourself' and (ironically) find yourself … um…lost. Now, if you are traveling, say, in England, you could simply find a local and ask for a phone, a map, a ride, or whatever to get where you need to go.

But you are all alone. And you are in the desert.

The heat is unbearable. The map you once had blew off in the wind a while back, but somehow that breeze has completely vanished. The stiff air seems to just increase the heat that is radiating all over your body. You stopped a while back to pet a friendly camel and all of a sudden have lost your sense of which direction you were headed. You would give anything for water, but it is long gone. Your lips are as dry as the dust and your throat is parched. You have ripped your clothing to shreds because it seemed (at the time) like it would make you cooler, but somehow all it is able to do is accentuate the sun on your skin and make you even hotter. You are hot and miserable, fading in and out of consciousness. This is miserable, and there is no hope is in sight.

Then it bursts into view: a large, beautiful, clean natural spring of crystal clear water and a large, leafy tree that gives off an infinitely greater amount of shade than it seems that it should.

Let those two images soak in: the dry, dusty, hot desert that whips the life out of you contrasted with the cool, flowing oasis that gives it back.

Life can feel like a desert, right? Our world is just plain tiring. With kids, jobs, hobbies, ministries, health issues, sports, finances and more, it can feel like we are meandering through a desert, lips parched, skin scorched, throat dry, body exhausted, no map and no breeze with our clothing in tatters. Not even a friendly camel to pet.

We need an oasis to remedy this. Your marriage needs one.

Let's cool off.

the word

¹²While the king was on his couch, my nard gave forth its fragrance. ¹³My beloved is to me a sachet of myrrh that lies between my breasts. ¹⁴My beloved is to me a cluster of henna blossoms in the vineyards of En-Gedi. ¹⁵Behold, you are beautiful, my love; behold, you are beautiful; your eyes are doves. ¹⁶Behold, you are beautiful, my beloved, truly delightful. Our couch is green; ¹⁷the beams of our house are cedar; our rafters are pine.

CHAPTER 2

¹I am a rose of Sharon, a lily of the valleys. ²As a lily among brambles, so is my love among the young women. ³As an apple tree among the trees of the forest, so is my beloved among the young men. With great delight I sat in his shadow, and his fruit was sweet to my taste. ⁴He brought me to the banqueting house, and his banner over me was love. ⁵Sustain me with raisins; refresh me with apples, for I am sick with love. ⁶His left hand is under my head, and his right hand embraces me! ⁷I adjure you, O daughters of Jerusalem, by the gazelles or the does of the field, that you not stir up or awaken love until it pleases. ⁸The voice of my beloved! Behold, he comes, leaping over the mountains, bounding over the hills. ⁹My beloved is like a gazelle or a young stag. Behold, there he stands behind our wall, gazing through the windows, looking through the lattice. ¹⁰My beloved speaks and says to me: "Arise, my love, my beautiful one, and come away, ¹¹for behold, the winter is past;

the word

the rain is over and gone. ¹²The flowers appear on the earth, the time of singing has come, and the voice of the turtledove is heard in our land. ¹³The fig tree ripens its figs, and the vines are in blossom; they give forth fragrance. Arise, my love, my beautiful one, and come away. ¹⁴O my dove, in the clefts of the rock, in the crannies of the cliff, let me see your face, let me hear your voice, for your voice is sweet, and your face is lovely. ¹⁵Catch the foxes for us, the little foxes that spoil the vineyards, for our vineyards are in blossom." ¹⁶My beloved is mine, and I am his; he grazes among the lilies.

DISCUSSION QUESTIONS

1. How would it change marriages if both partners became servant-lovers? Give examples, without being graphic.

_____
_____
_____
_____

2. In order to serve one another sexually, we must discuss sex. But some of us are uncomfortable with that. How can we overcome our discomfort?

_____
_____
_____
_____

> TECHNOLOGY HAS OVERTAKEN HUMAN CONTACT. WHEN YOU ARE TOGETHER, LOOK EACH OTHER IN THE EYE.

3. Thinking specifically of the crock pot-microwave example, how can husbands and wives better serve each other?

_____
_____
_____
_____

4. Married ladies only: Can you describe to some of the men how patience is beneficial in your relationship?

_____

_____

_____

_____

5. Certain sexual acts are "permissible but not mandatory" **within marriage**. How does a couple decide what they will and won't do together? (Earlier he talked about "oneness" versus "shame" as a filter.)

_____

_____

_____

_____

6. Ephesians 5:3 says, "But among you there must not be even a hint of sexual immorality." What are the implications of this for you as a single, as a married person, as a parent?

_____

_____

_____

_____

7. If "Where's the line?" is the wrong question, what is a better question and why is it important to know the difference?

_____

_____

_____

_____

SOME SMALL, INCONSEQUENTIAL THINGS CAN BE LITTLE FOXES IN THE VINEYARD THAT GROW AND GROW UNTIL THEY KILL THE RELATIONSHIP. LET THEM GO.

MEMORY VERSE

"As an apple tree among the trees of the forest, so is my beloved among the young men. With great delight I sat in his shadow, and his fruit was sweet to my taste."
(Song of Solomon 2:3, ESV)

application

Identify one specific action you will take as a result of this lesson. Write it down. If appropriate, share it with your small group.

_____

_____

_____

_____

homework

Follow through on your application point from the discussion time.

If married, discuss these questions as a couple:
- What does En-Gedi look like for us? How can we create that in our home? Our bedroom?
- What are the foxes that hinder our marriage from being all it can be? That keep us from enjoying En-Gedi?

- How can I be a better servant-lover?

If single, ask yourself:
- As I meet people, am I focused more on their character or on more superficial qualities? How can I be sure?
- What am I doing to cultivate godly character in myself?
- What foxes are in your vineyard?

NOTES

_____
_____
_____
_____
_____
_____
_____
_____
_____
_____
_____
_____
_____
_____

PRAYER requests

LOVELIFE

SESSION FOUR | foxes in the vineyard

SONG OF SOLOMON 2:15-16

A couple of my married friends went to Cuba on a mission trip and had a moment they will never forget. They got home from a long day of serving in the community, the wife slipped into the shower and the husband collapsed onto the bed. He turned on the baseball game but muted it when he started hearing something odd from the bathroom. It sounded like water hitting the floor. It was water hitting the floor.

Tons of it.

He looked in and saw his embarrassed wife wrapped in a towel and the floor covered with so much water that my friend debated building an ark. She had put the shower curtain on the outside of the tub instead of the inside.

Luckily, they weren't roughing it too badly, and the hotel had housekeepers that they could call to take care of this problem. The wife was mortified at her error (shower much?), though the couple was laughing like crazy at the absurdity of it.

But it got better.

Her husband knew Spanish pretty well, so he called the front desk. When the housekeeper arrived, the husband started explaining to her what happened. At one point, the wife asked her husband, "How do I say in Spanish that I am very embarrassed?" Before he could answer, she thought she knew and so she told the housekeeper, "Estoy embarazada". (Meaning "I am pregnant".)

So this maid, gets a call, walks up to the room of the stupid Americans who apparently can't use a shower, sees water all over the floor, and the wife keeps insistently saying "I am pregnant! I am pregnant!" I'm sure she was thinking, "We better get you to a doctor, then!"

It is important to know a language right? The slightest miscue in the language can make for quite an embarrassing situation. Just ask the higher-ups at Chevrolet when they rolled out a car named the *Nova*. The problem was that in Spanish, no va, literally means "it does not go", so the car did horribly in Spanish-speaking markets. Shocker.

Sometimes, when it comes to loving another person, we speak one language and they speak another. We mean one thing, but they hear another. It can be amusing at times, but it can also be painful on occasion when we are simply speaking two different languages. We need to learn our loved ones' languages.

Do we instinctively speak all the languages? No. Can we learn them? *Sí.*

the word

¹⁵Catch the foxes for us, the little foxes that spoil the vineyards, for our vineyards are in blossom." ¹⁶My beloved is mine, and I am his; he grazes among the lilies.

DISCUSSION QUESTIONS

1. Tell about a personality difference that causes friction between you and your spouse. It can be one that still causes friction or one that you have overcome. If the latter, how did you overcome it?

_____

_____

_____

_____

2. Describe a time when significant life events resulted in stress in your marriage. (e.g. illness, birth, job change, move)

_____

_____

_____

_____

> YOU ONLY HAVE TWO OPTIONS: EITHER JESUS DIED FOR THE SIN, OR THE MARRIAGE DIES BECAUSE OF THE SIN.

3. What were the five love languages referenced in the video?

1. _____

2. _____

3. _____

4. _____

5. _____

4. What is your spouse's love language? Is it the same as yours? Do you ever experience misunderstandings over this issue?

_____

_____

_____

_____

> you can never build intimacy on lies. you can't build oneness on sin.

5. Will time alone resolve any issues in a marriage? If not, then why do we see divorce statistics drop after 7 and 14 years, according to the DVD?

_____

_____

_____

_____

> some have their identity rooted in what was done to them, instead of what jesus did for them.

6. Why is it that sins of the **past** (both those we commit and those committed against us) are so devastating in the **present**?

_____

_____

_____

_____

Read 1 Peter 4:7-8 "The end of all things is near. Therefore be clear-minded and self-controlled so that you can pray. Above all, love each other deeply, because love covers over a multitude of sins." *As a group, pray together as couples for your homework time this week.*

MEMORY VERSE

"My beloved is mine, and I am his; he grazes among the lilies."
(Song of Solomon 2:16, ESV)

APPLICATION

Identify one specific action you will take as a result of this lesson. Write it down. If appropriate, share it with your small group.

_____

_____

_____

_____

DIVINGDEEPER

Consider reading *"the 5 Love Languages"*, as referenced in the video. (As of this writing, they are on Amazon for $10.19 new, and as little as $1.99 used.)

homework

Follow through on your application point from the discussion time. Commit ahead of time to work for each other's good and the good of your marriage. Ask each other, "What do I not know about you?" If appropriate, ask each other's forgiveness for past sins.

If married, discuss these questions as a couple:
- What are the issues that you and your spouse butt heads on?
- How can you resolve those issues?

NOTES

_____
_____
_____
_____
_____
_____
_____

PRAYERrequests

_____

_____

_____

_____

_____

_____

_____

LOVELIFE

SESSION FIVE | The wedding and the last day

SONG OF SOLOMON 3:6-5:1

Imagine, years from now, sitting out on your back porch in your favorite rocking chair, gently rocking back and forth with seemingly no care in the world.

It would be quiet, except for the shrieks of laughter emanating from some of your grandchildren that are running through the yard—a sound you are glad to have break your silence. You can't help it, and without thinking about it, a smile cuts across your face. It is a beautiful day out and you close your eyes in inhale deeply, savoring this moment as much as a man can.

Almost.

The afternoon is not perfect yet—something is still missing. Then, you hear the familiar creak of hinges from behind you, and the door opens. You don't need to even look to know that it is your wife, but you turn to look anyway, simply because you still want to.

Even after 40 years of marriage you still want to.

She hands you a glass of your favorite drink and sits next to you. Hand-in-hand you drink, talk, and beam with delight as you watch the scene before you.

Who wouldn't like that? The question is not whether or not you want that, but, Are you willing to pay the price to get that?

Are you living today by picturing the last half of your marriage, or are you so focused on today that you have no vision for tomorrow?

Let's look into the future.

the word

⁶What is that coming up from the wilderness like columns of smoke, perfumed with myrrh and frankincense, with all the fragrant powders of a merchant? ⁷Behold, it is the litter of Solomon! Around it are sixty mighty men, some of the mighty men of Israel, ⁸all of them wearing swords and expert in war, each with his sword at his thigh, against terror by night. ⁹King Solomon made himself a carriage from the wood of Lebanon. ¹⁰He made its posts of silver, its back of gold, its seat of purple; its interior was inlaid with love by the daughters of Jerusalem. ¹¹Go out, O daughters of Zion, and look upon King Solomon, with the crown with which his mother crowned him on the day of his wedding, on the day of the gladness of his heart.

CHAPTER 4

¹Behold, you are beautiful, my love, behold, you are beautiful! Your eyes are doves behind your veil. Your hair is like a flock of goats leaping down the slopes of Gilead. ²Your teeth are like a flock of shorn ewes that have come up from the washing, all of which bear twins, and not one among them has lost its young. ³Your lips are like a scarlet thread, and your mouth is lovely. Your cheeks are like halves of a pomegranate behind your veil. ⁴Your neck is like the tower of David, built in rows of stone; on it hang a thousand shields, all of them shields of warriors. ⁵Your two breasts are like two fawns, twins of a gazelle, that graze among the lilies. ⁶Until the day breathes and the shadows flee, I

will go away to the mountain of myrrh and the hill of frank-incense. ⁷You are altogether beautiful, my love; there is no flaw in you. ⁸Come with me from Lebanon, my bride; come with me from Lebanon. Depart from the peak of Amana, from the peak of Senir and Hermon, from the dens of lions, from the mountains of leopards. ⁹You have captivated my heart, my sister, my bride; you have captivated my heart with one glance of your eyes, with one jewel of your neck-lace. ¹⁰How beautiful is your love, my sister, my bride! How much better is your love than wine, and the fragrance of your oils than any spice! ¹¹Your lips drip nectar, my bride; honey and milk are under your tongue; the fragrance of your garments is like the fragrance of Lebanon. ¹²A garden locked is my sister, my bride, a spring locked, a fountain sealed. ¹³Your shoots are an orchard of pomegranates with all choicest fruits, henna with nard, ¹⁴nard and saffron, cal-amus and cinnamon, with all trees of frankincense, myrrh and aloes, with all choice spices— ¹⁵a garden fountain, a well of living water, and flowing streams from Lebanon. ¹⁶Awake, O north wind, and come, O south wind! Blow upon my garden, let its spices flow. Let my beloved come to his garden, and eat its choicest fruits.

CHAPTER 5

¹I came to my garden, my sister, my bride, I gathered my myrrh with my spice, I ate my honeycomb with my honey, I drank my wine with my milk. Eat, friends, drink, and be drunk with love!

DISCUSSION QUESTIONS

1. What did you do to prepare for your wedding? (flowers, invitations...)

_____

_____

_____

_____

2. What did you do to prepare for your marriage? (counseling, books...)

_____

_____

_____

_____

> BIBLICALLY, MARRIAGE IS;
> a) a covenant and b) consummation.

3. What do you wish you had known before you got married?

_____

_____

_____

_____

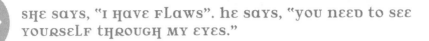

4. Describe your parents' marriage (or that of some other close, older relatives). What have you learned from their example, positive and negative?

_____

_____

_____

_____

5. A bit of a startling statement: That God would allow me to preach at Grace's funeral. What do you think is meant by this?

_____

_____

_____

_____

6. Read Ecclesiastes 7:8. How can the end of a marriage be better than its beginning? Describe what you hope your marriage will be like when you get old.

_____

_____

_____

_____

7. What kinds of things can you do now that will continue to improve your marriage? What will tend to tear it apart?

_____
_____
_____
_____

SHE IS NOT A PUBLIC PARK. SHE IS A PRIVATE GARDEN.

MEMORY VERSE

"You are altogether beautiful, my love; there is no flaw in you."
(Song of Solomon 4:7, ESV)

APPLICATION

Identify one specific action you will take as a result of this lesson. Write it down. If appropriate, share it with your small group.

_____

_____

_____

_____

DIVING DEEPER

The verses read today are some of the most touching and romantic in the Scriptures. Here are some more to look over, meditate upon, and read with your spouse:

- Genesis 29:1-20
- 1 Corinthians 13:4-7
- Colossians 3:12-14
- 1 John 3-4

homework

Follow through on your application point from the discussion time.

If married, discuss these questions as a couple:
- What do we want our old age together to look like?
- What can we do now to move us in that direction?

If it's not there already, put your wedding album out where you can get to it easily!

NOTES

_____

_____

_____

_____

_____

_____

_____

_____

_____

_____

_____

_____

PRAYER requests

_____

_____

_____

_____

_____

_____

_____

LOVELIFE

SESSION SIX | SIN'S DAMAGING EFFECTS

PASSAGES FROM ECCLESIASTES

Sin takes us farther down the path than we ever dreamed we'd go, and it keeps us far longer than we ever thought possible.

Satan and our flesh take us far from where we should be, little by little, in order to get us there. Let me illustrate.

It works like this:

- I'm just looking at the cheerleaders—who isn't?
- Sure I look at the swimsuit issue—no big deal!
- It's only naked girls in a magazine—it's not like they are even in the room with me!
- OK, so I look at Internet pornography—everyone knows that isn't even real!
- It's a strip club—it's not like I am having actual sex with them!
- It's only one affair...Wait! How did I get here?

That is how sin gets us. It moves us little by little until we are so far from where we want to be and so far from where we started that it shocks even us.

Sin moves us subtly in small increments to get us to commit greater and greater sin.

Ask the captain of a ship if he was traveling around the world, how big a deal it is being off by only a half of a degree. He won't notice right away how far off course he is. But over time, he is not even close to where he needs to be.

Just let a little sin enter. Soon you won't believe how far off you are.

DISCUSSION QUESTIONS

1. What kinds of sexual sin were parts of Solomon's later life? What parallels can you draw to the world we live in? How do they affect your views on marriage and how you relate to your spouse?

_____
_____
_____
_____

2. What is the popular cultural view of pornography? Extra-marital sex? Abortion?)

_____
_____
_____
_____

> You cannot manage sin. You cannot constrain sin. Sin grows, multiplies, and leads to death.

3. What happens when we take a casual attitude toward sex, sexuality, and morality? What are the results for people personally and society as a whole?

_____
_____
_____
_____

4. How has your own attitude toward sexual morality changed over the years? Are you more or less casual about sexual sin? Why?

_____

_____

_____

_____

5. Sexual sin destroys marriages. According to the secular research cited in the DVD, what tends to protect marriages? Why do you think this is so?

_____

_____

_____

_____

6. Why do Christian women marry men who are "Christian, but don't go to church"? What assumptions are they making and why?

_____

_____

_____

_____

7. Couples, how often do you go to church together? How often do you pray together? What difference does it make in your marriage?

_____

_____

_____

_____

8. Discuss the comment, "Men **are** the spiritual leaders of their homes. The question is whether they are good or bad at their jobs."

_____

_____

_____

_____

WHEN THE BIBLE COMMANDS US MEN TO BE ONE-WOMAN-MEN, IT IS FOR OUR GOOD. GOD IS NOT WITHHOLDING FROM YOU ANY GOOD THING.

9. If a husband is not doing a good job of leading his family spiritually, what should his wife do?

_____

_____

_____

_____

MEMORY VERSE

"I said in my heart, 'Come now, I will test you with pleasure; enjoy yourself.' But behold, this also was vanity. " (Ecclesiastes 2:1, ESV)

application

Identify one specific action you will take as a result of this lesson. Write it down. If appropriate, share it with your small group.

_____

_____

_____

_____

homework

Follow through on your application point from the discussion time.

If married, discuss this question as a couple:
   • What is one thing we could do together to pursue Jesus?

NOTES

_____
_____
_____
_____
_____
_____
_____
_____
_____
_____
_____
_____
_____
_____
_____
_____
_____
_____
_____
_____
_____
_____

PRAYER requests

_____

_____

_____

_____

_____

_____

_____

LOVELIFE

SESSION SEVEN | The fight

SONG OF SOLOMON 5:2-6:3

There is *nothing* like a good fight.

As I think back to the movies that many men especially like, they usually revolve around colossal conflict. It is usually nation against nation, an oppressed people rising up against their oppressors, or just a group of men against another group of men—no explanation necessary.

We love seeing the rousing speeches before they go to battle *(Lord of the Rings)*, the thousands of archers sending a barrage of arrows at the enemy in unison *(Gladiator)*, and huge masses of humanity lined up on either end of a field, charging at each other *(Braveheart)*. The chaos and gratuitous violence that ensues is exactly why we bought the ticket in the first place. Sometimes it is an even match *(Star Trek)*, and sometimes it is a small group against an entire empire *(300)*. Either way, we love to watch the fight.

No matter the odds, the actors, the quality of effects, or the actual plot, we turn out to see these movies in droves. There is just something about a good fight…

Unless you are the one in it.

Then…it's not so fun.

the word

SONG OF SOLOMON
5:2-14

²I slept, but my heart was awake. A sound! My beloved is knocking." Open to me, my sister, my love, my dove, my perfect one, for my head is wet with dew, my locks with the drops of the night." ³I had put off my garment; how could I put it on? I had bathed my feet; how could I soil them? ⁴My beloved put his hand to the latch, and my heart was thrilled within me. ⁵I arose to open to my beloved, and my hands dripped with myrrh, my fingers with liquid myrrh, on the handles of the bolt. ⁶I opened to my beloved, but my beloved had turned and gone. My soul failed me when he spoke. I sought him, but found him not; I called him, but he gave no answer. ⁷The watchmen found me as they went about in the city; they beat me, they bruised me, they took away my veil, those watchmen of the walls. ⁸I adjure you, O daughters of Jerusalem, if you find my beloved, that you tell him I am sick with love. ⁹What is your beloved more than another beloved, O most beautiful among women? What is your beloved more than another beloved, that you thus adjure us? ¹⁰My beloved is radiant and ruddy, distinguished among ten thousand. ¹¹His head is the finest gold; his locks are wavy, black as a raven. ¹²His eyes are like doves beside streams of water, bathed in milk, sitting beside a full pool. ¹³His cheeks are like beds of spices, mounds of sweet-smelling herbs. His lips are lilies, dripping liquid myrrh. ¹⁴His arms are rods of gold, set with jewels. His body is polished ivory, bedecked with sapphires. ¹⁵His

the word

legs are alabaster columns, set on bases of gold. His appearance is like Lebanon, choice as the cedars. [16]His mouth is most sweet, and he is altogether desirable. This is my beloved and this is my friend, O daughters of Jerusalem.

CHAPTER 6

[1]Where has your beloved gone, O most beautiful among women? Where has your beloved turned, that we may seek him with you? [2]My beloved has gone down to his garden to the beds of spices, to graze in the gardens and to gather lilies. [3]I am my beloved's and my beloved is mine; he grazes among the lilies.

DISCUSSION QUESTIONS

1. Of the ways to respond to a conflict—flee, shut down, push for resolution, win at all costs, etc.—do men and women, as a group, tend to lean toward one of these ways? What about you? What is *your* natural response to conflict?

_____

_____

_____

_____

2. Why is conflict an expected part of a good marriage?

_____

_____

_____

_____

> I'M ALWAYS WORRIED WHEN SOMEONE SAYS, "WE NEVER FIGHT". THAT MEANS YOU STOPPED CARING A LONG TIME AGO.

3. Explain this comment, "A man can't win when he fights with his wife". What will most men do instead?

_____

_____

_____

_____

4. *Women:* What is a prudent response when your husband walks away from an argument with you?

_____

_____

_____

_____

5. When a couple fights, who should they talk with about it? Who should they not talk with about it? Why?

_____

_____

_____

_____

> THERE IS NO WAY FOR A MAN TO WIN A FIGHT WITH HIS WIFE. IF YOU WIN, YOU LOSE. IF YOU LOSE, YOU LOSE. EVERY GUY KNOWS THAT.

6. Why do couples need to place importance on being friends with each other? What does that involve—what does it look like?

_____

_____

_____

_____

7. Describe the marriage of two servant-lovers. What kind of a marriage will two selfish people have?

_____

_____

_____

_____

8. Is there a difference between 'serving' and being a 'servant'?

_____

_____

_____

_____

"LOVER" AND "FRIEND": THE TRUTH IS THAT MOST OF YOUR LIFE WITH YOUR SPOUSE ISN'T SPENT AS 'LOVER'. IT IS SPENT AS 'FRIEND'.

9. Why is it so hard to choose to be a servant?

_____

_____

_____

_____

MEMORY VERSE

"Where has your lover gone, most beautiful of women? Which way did your lover turn, that we may look for him with you?" (Song of Solomon 6:1, ESV)

aPPLication

Identify one specific action you will take as a result of this lesson. Write it down. If appropriate, share it with your small group.

_____

_____

_____

_____

homework

Follow through on your application point from the discussion time.

If married, discuss this question as a couple:
- How well do I serve you?
- How could I serve you better?
- In what way(s) am I selfish in our relationship?

Who are some people that you as a couple can agree to talk with if you are in a fight? Who are people you should not talk with?

NOTES

_____

_____

_____

_____

_____

_____

_____

_____

_____

_____

_____

_____

_____

_____

_____

_____

_____

PRAYER requests

_____

_____

_____

_____

_____

_____

_____

LOVELIFE

SESSION EIGHT | servant lovers

SONG OF SOLOMON 5:2-6:3

There is a great, rarely told story in Exodus 21.

We frequently skip over it, and I'm afraid it is often neglected because it deals with the oh-so exciting topic of laws regarding Hebrew slaves. Fun.

Verses 2-4 declare that a servant must serve his master for six years, but gets to go free in the seventh. Any wife he had when he became a slave gets to go free as well—no penalty.

But in verse 5 we see something perplexing, yet beautiful. If a slave declares that he loves his master, wife, and children and does not want to go free, he goes before a judge (so it can be official) and pledges himself to that owner for life. The owner takes him publicly to the doorpost and pierces his ear with an awl. And for all his days, the slave bears the mark that publicly declares that he will willingly serve this one that he loves.

What a picture of marriage!

If a man decides he loves a woman and determines that he will serve her for life, he publicly declares it. The public sign is not ear-piercing, but rings. We don't talk about marriages like that do we?

We talk about marriage in terms of love, but rarely service. The bride and groom need to understand that what they enter into is a commitment to serve the other for life, first and foremost.

I think the next wedding I do, instead of asking for the rings, I will ask the best man, "Do you have the awl".

I'll whip out a doorpost and see if they still wanna do this thing...

the word

²I slept, but my heart was awake. A sound! My beloved is knocking." Open to me, my sister, my love, my dove, my perfect one, for my head is wet with dew, my locks with the drops of the night." ³I had put off my garment; how could I put it on? I had bathed my feet; how could I soil them? ⁴My beloved put his hand to the latch, and my heart was thrilled within me. ⁵I arose to open to my beloved, and my hands dripped with myrrh, my fingers with liquid myrrh, on the handles of the bolt. ⁶I opened to my beloved, but my beloved had turned and gone. My soul failed me when he spoke. I sought him, but found him not; I called him, but he gave no answer. ⁷The watchmen found me as they went about in the city; they beat me, they bruised me, they took away my veil, those watchmen of the walls. ⁸I adjure you, O daughters of Jerusalem, if you find my beloved, that you tell him I am sick with love. ⁹What is your beloved more than another beloved, O most beautiful among women? What is your beloved more than another beloved, that you thus adjure us? ¹⁰My beloved is radiant and ruddy, distinguished among ten thousand. ¹¹His head is the finest gold; his locks are wavy, black as a raven. ¹²His eyes are like doves beside streams of water, bathed in milk, sitting beside a full pool. ¹³His cheeks are like beds of spices, mounds of sweet-smelling herbs. His lips are lilies, dripping liquid myrrh. ¹⁴His arms are rods of gold, set with jewels. His body is polished ivory, bedecked with sapphires. ¹⁵His

the word

legs are alabaster columns, set on bases of gold. His appearance is like Lebanon, choice as the cedars. ¹⁶His mouth is most sweet, and he is altogether desirable. This is my beloved and this is my friend, O daughters of Jerusalem.

CHAPTER 6

¹Where has your beloved gone, O most beautiful among women? Where has your beloved turned, that we may seek him with you? ²My beloved has gone down to his garden to the beds of spices, to graze in the gardens and to gather lilies. ³I am my beloved's and my beloved is mine; he grazes among the lilies.

DISCUSSION QUESTIONS

1. What causes conflict in marriage? What kinds of things do people fight about?

_____

_____

_____

_____

2. What role does selfishness play in conflict?

_____

_____

_____

_____

(For group discussion, keep your examples non-sexual for the first two questions.)

3. What is one way that you are selfish that causes conflict in your marriage?

_____

_____

_____

_____

4. What would it look like to become a servant to your spouse in that area?

_____

_____

_____

_____

> FUNDAMENTALLY DRILLED DOWN IN OUR IDENTITY IS RADICAL, RUTHLESS INDEPENDENCE.

5. How does selfishness affect our discussions about conflict and sex? How could being servant-lovers to each other affect these conversations?

_____

_____

_____

_____

> CONFESSION IS WHERE WE AGREE WITH GOD THAT WHAT WE DID WAS WRONG.

6. How do you respond to the statement, "Selfishness in marriage is a sin"? Is this a new idea for you?

_____

_____

_____

_____

7. Which of the steps for dealing with your sin comes easiest for you? Which is hardest? Why?

• Conviction (naming the sin)

_____

_____

• Confession (to God and spouse)

_____

_____

• Repentance (put this sin to death)

_____

_____

• Restitution (pay back what is owed)

_____

_____

• Reconciliation (renew the relationship)

_____

_____

WHEN YOU SIN AGAINST YOUR SPOUSE, LOOK THEM IN THE EYE AND NAME YOUR SIN.

YOU KNOW THAT SOMEONE IS REPENTANT WHEN YOU SEE CHANGE.

application

Identify one specific action you will take as a result of this lesson. Write it down. If appropriate, share it with your small group.

_____

_____

_____

_____

homework

Follow through on your application point from the discussion time.

Identify an area in which you have been selfish toward your spouse, then recognize it as sin, and take appropriate action (conviction, confession, repentance, restitution, reconciliation).

PRAYER requests

_____

_____

_____

_____

LOVELIFE

SESSION NINE | VISUAL AND VERBAL GENEROSITY

SONG OF SOLOMON 6:4-7:13

When you buy a car, it is understood that some work goes along with it.

When you first purchase the car, there is a manual in every glove box that has a schedule of maintenance that should be performed on the car. Each car has detailed instructions from the manufacturer about what to do at all the different mileage increments, giving detailed instructions on what to do with every belt, filter, and hose. Then you need to get the oil changed regularly and keep an eye on the PSI of your tires, plus the levels on the washer, power steering, and brake fluids. All this is to make sure the car runs smoothly for a long period of time. No one wants to buy a new car every month.

The simple reason is that we pay a lot of money for our automobiles, and so we want them to last a while. And if you want them to last a long time, you must go through the trouble of reading the manual and maintaining them.

It is imperative that you follow the book given by the manufacturer if you want it to last and last well.

The same is true in marriage.

How do you make a marriage last and last well? There are few passages in the Bible that answer that question better than the one we are looking at today.

Consider this the maintenance manual of marriage.

the word

⁴You are beautiful as Tirzah, my love, lovely as Jerusalem, awesome as an army with banners. ⁵Turn away your eyes from me, for they overwhelm me— Your hair is like a flock of goats leaping down the slopes of Gilead. ⁶Your teeth are like a flock of ewes that have come up from the washing; all of them bear twins; not one among them has lost its young. ⁷Your cheeks are like halves of a pomegranate behind your veil. ⁸There are sixty queens and eighty concubines, and virgins without number. ⁹My dove, my perfect one, is the only one, the only one of her mother, pure to her who bore her. The young women saw her and called her blessed; the queens and concubines also, and they praised her. ¹⁰"Who is this who looks down like the dawn, beautiful as the moon, bright as the sun, awesome as an army with banners?" ¹¹I went down to the nut orchard to look at the blossoms of the valley, to see whether the vines had budded, whether the pomegranates were in bloom. ¹²Before I was aware, my desire set me among the chariots of my kinsman, a prince. ¹³Return, return, O Shulammite, return, return, that we may look upon you. Why should you look upon the Shulammite, as upon a dance before two armies?

CHAPTER 7

¹How beautiful are your feet in sandals, O noble daughter! Your rounded thighs are like jewels, the work of a master hand. ²Your navel is a rounded bowl that never lacks mixed

the word

wine. Your belly is a heap of wheat, encircled with lilies. ³Your two breasts are like two fawns, twins of a gazelle. ⁴Your neck is like an ivory tower. Your eyes are pools in Heshbon, by the gate of Bath-rabbim. Your nose is like a tower of Lebanon, which looks toward Damascus. ⁵Your head crowns you like Carmel, and your flowing locks are like purple; a king is held captive in the tresses. ⁶How beautiful and pleasant you are, O loved one, with all your delights! ⁷Your stature is like a palm tree, and your breasts are like its clusters. ⁸I say I will climb the palm tree and lay hold of its fruit. Oh may your breasts be like clusters of the vine, and the scent of your breath like apples, ⁹and your mouth like the best wine. It goes down smoothly for my beloved, gliding over lips and teeth. ¹⁰I am my beloved's, and his desire is for me. ¹¹Come, my beloved, let us go out into the fields and lodge in the villages; ¹²let us go out early to the vineyards and see whether the vines have budded, whether the grape blossoms have opened and the pomegranates are in bloom. There I will give you my love. ¹³The mandrakes give forth fragrance, and beside our doors are all choice fruits, new as well as old, which I have laid up for you, O my beloved.

DISCUSSION QUESTIONS

1. What is your reaction to the information that men are so visually oriented? Are you surprised, relieved, uncomfortable...?

_____

_____

_____

_____

2. What is the difference between temptation and sin? Why is it important to recognize this distinction?

_____

_____

_____

_____

> THERE IS A HUGE DIFFERENCE BETWEEN TEMPTATION AND SIN.

3. _Men_, how can your wife be a sympathetic ally to you in your battle against lust? Have you invited her help in this area?

_____

_____

_____

_____

4. Women, what challenges could you face as your husband's ally in this battle?

_____

_____

_____

_____

> MEN HAVE A ROLODEX OF IMAGES. A WIFE CAN GIVE HIM REDEEMED IMAGES.

5. Many women are uncomfortable with being "visually generous" toward their husbands. (That is, they're shy about being naked and 'erotic' towards them.) Why do you think this is? How can this shyness be misunderstood by the husband? How can women overcome this?

_____

_____

_____

_____

6. Some men are uncomfortable with being verbally generous toward their wives. (They hesitate to give compliments.) Why do you think this is? How can this silence be misunderstood by the wife?

_____

_____

_____

_____

7. *Women*, do you give the same attention to your appearance for your husband that you did when you were dating?

_____

_____

_____

_____

> habituate your body to greatly enjoy your spouse.

8. *Men*, do you praise, compliment, and encourage your wife the way you did when you were dating?

_____

_____

_____

_____

9. What can you do to place a priority on being alone together, as a couple? (Dates, vacations, long walks...) What would you each need to sacrifice to make that happen?

_____

_____

_____

_____

> christians should never fall into the trap of accepting a mediocre marriage.

MEMORY VERSE

"I belong to my lover, and his desire is for me." (Song of Solomon 7:10, ESV)

application

Identify one specific action you will take as a result of this lesson. Write it down. If appropriate, share it with your small group.

_____

_____

_____

_____

DIVING DEEPER

With your spouse, read aloud and meditate on **Hebrews 4:15**.

homework

Follow through on your application point from the discussion time.

Wives, ask your husband, What are your favorite images of me? (or, How do you like to see me?)

Men, ask your wife, How can I be more verbally generous with you? (or, What do you like to hear me say?)

Notes

_____
_____
_____
_____
_____
_____
_____
_____
_____
_____
_____
_____

PRAYER requests

_____

_____

_____

_____

_____

_____

_____

LOVELIFE

SESSION TEN | QUESTION & ANSWER

One of my favorite times at the conferences is when I get to know the specific needs and questions of the people that I get to teach.

Here is a session devoted entirely to questions and answers from the conference. I wish we had time for dozens, but time doesn't permit.

Do any of them resonate?

QUESTIONS FROM THE VIDEO

1. What do I do if my wife wants sex more than I do and I feel like less of a man?

2. If you are dating someone who is not a Christian and doesn't have the best reputation, but is willing to go to church with you, is it okay?

3. My wife says she never has been in love with me and married me because of our son. What advice would you have?

> LADIES, YOUR HUSBAND IS MUCH MORE FRAIL AND FRAGILE THAN YOU CAN IMAGINE.

4. Is birth control biblical?

5. What do you do with a husband that will not lead?

6. My husband and I had sex prior to marriage and feel the intensity we had prior to marriage isn't there. How do we find it again?

> YOU CAN'T LOVE PASSIONATELY, DEEPLY AND THOROUGHLY WITHOUT GOD'S LOVE.

7. I did something in the past that hurt my wife emotionally. Every time we fight I give in to her, but I feel like a lesser man.

8. My best friend's wife dresses in a very revealing way. She acts oblivious, like it is no big deal. I can't help but notice and it makes my wife angry.

9. My wife of twelve years will not stay in the same room as me. No sex for over a year. Is she unfaithful?

▶ YOU DON'T NEED A NEW SPOUSE, YOU NEED A NEW MARRIAGE.

▶ CHRISTIAN 'DIVORCE' (LIVING SEPARATE LIVES UNDER THE SAME ROOF) IS OBEYING THE LETTER OF THE LAW, WHILE DISREGARDING THE SPIRIT OF IT. AND YOUR CHILDREN ARE WITNESSING A FALSE GOSPEL.

DIVINGDEEPER

What question would you have added to the above list? How can you go about finding the answer to that question?

application

Identify one specific action you will take as a result of this lesson. Write it down. If appropriate, share it with your small group.

_____

_____

_____

_____

homework

Follow through on your application point from the discussion time.

If married, discuss this question as a couple:
- Which questions resonated with us?
- Which ones do we need to discuss in a frank but loving manner?

PRAYER requests

_____

_____

_____

_____

_____

_____

_____

LOVELIFE

BEHIND THE BOOK | song of solomon

BeHiNd The BOOK

INTRODUCTION
The 22nd book in the Old Testament, the Song of Solomon, is often referred to as the *Song of Songs* as well, the name being a Hebrew superlative, the same way in which the Bible speaks of the "King of Kings", "Lord of Lords", or "Holy of Holies". "The title the *Song of Songs* is a Hebrew idiom meaning 'The Most Excellent Song'."[1] This supreme song has been "breathed out by God" (2 Tim. 3:16) and preserved for centuries in our biblical canon by God's good grace with timeless truths for us all.

THE AUTHOR
Immediately in the title we see that the author of the *Song of Solomon* appears to be Solomon, but is it really that simple? There are numerous reasons to take the author as Solomon, or at the least someone transcribing the thoughts of the great king of Israel. Solomon, the son of David and third king of Israel, is named in the book as author and his name appears seven times in the text (1:1, 5; 3:7, 9, 11; 8:11, 12). There are characteristics of the book that make it very natural to assume that Solomon was the author as well. "The fact that Solomon was known for his wisdom and poetry (1 Kings 4:29-34) partially substantiates his authorship of this book."[2] "The allusions to nature fit in with Solomon's interests (1 Kings 4:33). Also, references to royal horses, and the palanquin tend to support Solomonic authorship. The geographical references suggest that the places were all in one united kingdom, which was true chiefly during Solomon's reign. Thus, there is every reason to accept the traditional view of authorship, and contrary arguments are not convincing."[3]

The evidence points us to Solomon as author of this book, inspired by the Spirit of God like every other biblical author (2 Peter 1:21). "King Solomon probably wrote this loveliest of his 1,005 songs (1 Kings 4:32) some time during his forty year reign (971-931 BC)."[4] What we will soon see is that the book written by someone thousands of years ago and thousands of miles away is still incredibly relevant for us today.

INTERPRETIVE APPROACHES
How to properly read the *Song of Songs* has been debated by scholars and theologians for centuries. Over the years it has been interpreted several different ways, though the different interpretations can be put into four broad categories: cultic/mythological, dramatic, allegorical/symbolic, and natural/literal.[5]

---

[1] William MacDonald, *Believer's Bible Commentary*, ed. Art Farstad (Nashville: Thomas Nelson Publishers, 1995), 919.

[2] Earl Radmacher, Ronald B. Allen, and H. Wayne House, ed., *Nelson's New Illustrated Bible Commentary* (Nashville: Nelson, 1999), 795.

[3] MacDonald, *Believer's Bible Commentary*, 919-20.

[4] Ibid., 920.

[5] Dennis F. Kinlaw, "Song of Songs," in *The Expositor's Bible Commentary*, ed. Frank E. Gaebelein, vol. 5. 12 vols. (Grand Rapids: Zondervan, 1991), 1202-05.

BehindTheBOOK

Cultic/Mythological

This argument to interpret the *Song of Solomon* as mythological or cultic is by far the least popular of the four opinions. "According to this view, the poem does not really speak of human love at all; rather, *it is either the celebration of the sacred marriage of a goddess in the person of a priestess with the king, or else it is the celebration of the victory of the divine king over death and drought.*"[6] This approach was originally put forth by self-proclaimed polytheists, and their opinions need to be understood in light of that presupposition. I only mention this position briefly, as most evangelical scholarship today ignores it completely. The main three interpretations by scholars today follow.

Dramatic

As we read the *Song of Solomon*, certainly there is a sense that what is unfolding before our eyes in the text is a drama. After all, we see romance, love, desire, a 'hero', and pursuit all in the few short chapters as we watch these characters interact. But the term 'drama' in this sense does not mean a formal drama, synonymous with a 'play' that was meant to be acted out on a stage, but rather a literary form that simply means it is dramatic in nature. One commentator, when referring to the *Song of Songs* as a drama clarifies by stating, "I do not use the term 'drama' necessarily to imply that the text is written for enactment by actors, whether in a royal court or worship. The *Song of Songs* clearly has a dramatic form, even if only as a romantic drama between two lovers."[7]

Though it is difficult to argue the point that, by form, the *Song of Songs* is clearly dramatic[8] the interpretations that would fall into this view are those that state, "The *Song of Songs* was nothing more than a drama or a play to be acted out".

This position is not without its problems, as "there has been no consistency in the development of this view. Absence of stage directions, lack of agreement on how many characters, or who said what, the lack of any clear signs of division into 'acts' or 'scenes', and the fact that the dramatic form never really caught on in the East have prevented this approach from gaining any extensive support."[9] Also, it is rightly pointed out that with regards to the form of a dramatic play, "there is no evidence apart from the Song that this kind of literature existed in Israel".[10]

---

[6]Ibid., 1205.

[7] Iain Provan, *The NIV Application Commentary, Ecclesiastes/Song of Songs* (Grand Rapids: Zondervan, 2001), 245.

[8]Charles Dyer, and Eugene Merrill, *Nelson's Old Testament Survey* (Nashville: Thomas Nelson, 2001), 512.

[9]Kinlaw, "Song of Songs.", 1204-1205.

[10]David and Pat Alexander, ed., *Eerdman's Handbook to the Bible* (Grand Rapids: William B. Eerdman's Publishing Company, 1983), 367.

Behind The BOOK

The book contains a dramatic story, with dramatic characters and other dramatic elements, but it does not appear to be intended to be read as a drama in the sense of having been prepared for actors and a stage. This position is generally rejected in evangelical scholarship today.

Allegorical/Symbolic

A strong case can be made (and has been made) that the best interpretation of this book is allegorical in nature. Kinlaw points out that "the oldest documented interpretation of the *Song of Songs* sees it as allegory. This position was well-established by the first century of the Christian era and has had a long and illustrious history in both Judaism and Christianity."[11] Provan argues, "The allegorical reading of the *Song of Songs* is probably at least as old as the literal reading."[12]

The allegorical approach essentially says that the book does not portray actual events rooted in history, but is entirely a symbolic narrative. Some have seen it as a "parable glorifying human and divine love, an Israelite allegory teaching God's love for Israel, or a Christian allegory revealing His love for the Church."[13] The Catholic Church at one point had even identified the bride in the Songs as the Virgin Mary.

Is it possible to read the text as an allegory? Can we see the book as a picture of the love of God for the Church? "The usual Christian interpretation given to this book is that it represents the love of Christ for His Church…According to this view, Solomon is a type of Christ and the Shulamite a type of the Church. However, the careful student of Scripture will realize that this cannot be the primary interpretation of the book since the Church was a secret, hidden in God from the foundation of the world and not revealed until the apostles and the prophets of the New Testament (Romans 16:25, 26; Ephesians 3:9)."[14] It is difficult to take the primary interpretation of the book as allegorical love between Christ and the Church, as the Church would not be revealed for another 1,000 years.

Scores of other commentators concur and point out that it is oddly written if it is meant as simply allegorical. "It is somewhat difficult to believe that an ancient Hebrew author primarily intent on speaking on a relationship between God and God's people would have composed the *Song of Songs* in precisely the way that he or

---

[11] Kinlaw, "Song of Songs," 1202.

[12] Provan, *The NIV Application Commentary, Ecclesiastes/Song of Songs*, 238.

[13] Dyer, *Nelson's Old Testament Survey*, 512.

[14] MacDonald, *Believer's Bible Commentary*, 920.

she did, with such heavy emphasis on the erotic aspects of love and particular passages such as 8:5b-7, where the woman (i.e., on this reading, the people of God) takes the initiative in "rousing" the man's (i.e., God's) love."[15] In other words, the more 'intimate' portions of the text can be somewhat symbolic, but why go into the details of the erotic love between the two, which obviously does not parallel the metaphor of Christ and the Church?

Great caution must be taken as one undertakes to study this book (or any other biblical text for that matter) as a solely symbolic allegory. "While the *Song of Songs* illustrates the deepening love we have with Christ, we must be careful not to turn the story into an allegory and make everything mean something. All things are possible to those who allegorize—and what they come up with is usually heretical. It's almost laughable to read some of the ancient commentaries (and their modern imitators) and see how interpreters have made Solomon say what they want him to say."[16]

Since many ancient and contemporary evangelical scholars have seen this is, in some sense, a plausible interpretation, an allegorical approach must be given some consideration, though we must proceed down this road with great caution. I would offer that if someone wanted to teach on the love of God for His people to go to other texts (1 John 4:7-21, Romans 8:35-39) that speak to that great truth explicitly. This method of interpretation can, at best, be secondary to a natural/literal interpretation.

Natural/Literal
This approach views the people as real and the events as literal. This is the natural way to understand the text, so if someone wants to take the book as other than literal, the burden is on them to make their case. So far, the cases against a literal approach fall far short. *The Nelson's New Illustrated Bible Commentary*, for example, starts out by simply claiming, "The *Song of Solomon* is a moving love story between a young country girl and King Solomon."[17] These commentators assume right off the bat that the author is literally Solomon writing about an actual young woman.

---

[15] Provan, *The NIV Application Commentary, Ecclesiastes/Song of Songs*, 241.

[16] Warren Wiersbe, *The Bible Exposition Commentary: Old Testament Wisdom and History* (Colorado Springs: Victor, 2003), 542.

[17] Radmacher, ed., *Nelson's New Illustrated Bible Commentary*, 793.

BehiNdTheBOOK

"Whatever *application* this love story may have to God's relation to His people, or Christ's love for His church, it seems better to insist on a literal *interpretation* of this book for the following two basic reasons. First, it is inconsistent to allegorize this story and insist on taking the Gospels and other parts of Scripture literally. Second, taking it literally does not contradict any other teaching of Scripture. Rather, it complements it in many ways. God instituted marriage (Gen. 2:23-24). God created sex and gave it to humans to enjoy within the bonds of marriage (Gen. 1:27; Prov. 5:17-19). Paul declared that sex should be exercised within monogamous marriage (1 Cor. 7:1-5). Timothy was informed that sex within marriage should not be forbidden (1 Tim. 4:14) and that God 'gives us richly all things to enjoy' (1 Tim. 6:17). The Song of Solomon is a beautiful example of real romance between two actual people that extols the biblical view of sex and marriage" (emphasis his).[18]

Conclusion

So it seems upon this research that the natural approach is the best way to read this book, if the four must be done exclusively of each other. So do the four approaches need to be exclusive of each other? If the best reading of the text is a literal approach, is any part of this text in any way an allegory or a picture of things that existed then (God and Israel) or things to come (God and the Church)? Perhaps there are two levels at which this needs to be read: literal (natural) and allegorical. It seems apparent that the natural approach is vital and primary, but "it is impossible to rule out allegory (or at least a second and deeper sense of the text) as one aspect of the text's intentionality."[19]

It seems that the allegorical approach makes sense in some form, but not as a primary method of interpretation, and certainly not as an exclusive one. Does an author have to only have one purpose in writing, especially when the author is ultimately divine? Is not the Holy Spirit wise enough to move a human to write a book that can be read on multiple levels? Provan again says, "an author need not have only one aim in writing or only one intention in the words they use. Why can the text not be assumed in its original intention to be both about human love and about

---

[18] Norman Geisler, and Thomas Howe, *When Critics Ask: A Popular Handbook on Bible Difficulties* (Grand Rapids: Baker Books, 1999), 263-64.

[19] Provan, *The NIV Application Commentary, Ecclesiastes/Song of Songs*, 241.

divine-human love?"[20] "The New Testament uses the same metaphor positively. Ephesians 5:22-33 teaches that the relationship between a man and his wife is analog to the relationship between Jesus and the Church. The intimacy of marriage pictures the intimacy of God's love for us. It is thus not inappropriate to read the *Song of Solomon* as a poem reflecting on the relationship between God and His people, as long as the primary reference to human sexuality is not repressed."[21] "While the primary reference is to human sexuality, the book does teach us about our relationship with God."[22]

I therefore believe that the best way to understand that authorial intent of this book is to understand that it has some dramatic elements, but it is not intended to be acted out as a play. It has some allegorical elements that are to be taken very carefully and compared against the rest of Scripture to determine the soundness of the interpretation. "Without the literal sense as an anchor, it has always been too easy for men to sail the good ship of allegory wherever they wished, avoiding those things in the ocean that they did not wish to comprehend."[23]

A literal reading of the love between a man and a woman seems to be the primary means of understanding this wonderful book of the sacred Scriptures, with room left for seeing the text as, secondarily, a picture of the love between God and Israel and/or Christ and the Church.

PURPOSE

The *Song of Solomon* is a profound story about love between a man and a woman. Today we need to hear this story repeatedly and let it soak in our souls and permeate our thoughts and actions with regards to love, sex, romance, and marriage. This book is an incredible "canonical corrective to the perversion of sexuality"[24] that is prevalent in our society today. Our culture is driven by sex and relationships, and God in His goodness provided a moving story to give us an example of how it should work according to the Designer.

---

[20]Ibid., 241-42.

[21]Tremper III and Raymond B. Dillard Longman, *An Introduction to the Old Testament* (Grand Rapids: Zondervan, 2006), 300.

[22] Ibid.

[23] Provan, *The NIV Application Commentary, Ecclesiastes/Song of Songs*, 247.

[24] Longman, *An Introduction to the Old Testament*, 299.

Behind The BOOK

It is obvious from this book that sex does not make God blush. "While certain Jews and Christians have prudishly avoided the book as 'sensual', some of the most devout saints throughout history have reveled in its pages."[25] So should we.

Why so much sex-talk in the sacred Scriptures? "If the Bible is the book about God, then one may well ask what a narrative about human sexuality has to do with theology. This is an even more potent question when one notes that God is never mentioned in the entire text (except possibly in 8:6) nor are there any references to prayer, worship, or piety...To resolve this difficulty, it is important to remember that the Bible not only describes who God is and what God does; it also tells us what God desires for His people. The *Song of Solomon* provides an example of how God created male and female to live in happiness and fulfillment."[26] If we want to truly live the Christian life to the fullest, we must have a deep understanding of how to live like a Christian with the opposite sex. The *Song of Solomon* is a marvelous text in the Scriptures to help us do that exact thing.

This book can move us in our faith and deepen our love for the Lord as well. "The major theme of this book is human love between a man and a woman. Many striking images communicate that this love is sensual, intimate, exclusive, and important. Since the broader canon describes our relationship with God as a marriage, the more we learn about married love, the more we also learn about our relationship with our divine spouse."[27]

So, open this book. Study its truth, enjoy its precepts, and revel in the freedom found there. Most importantly, exalt the Creator to which it points us, and then proclaim the life it gives to the dying world, now more than ever.

---

[25] MacDonald, *Believer's Bible Commentary*, 919.

[26] Radmacher, ed., *Nelson's New Illustrated Bible Commentary*, 795.

[27] Tremper Longman III, *Song of Songs*, vol. 6, 18 vols., Cornerstone Biblical Commentary, ed. PhilipW. Comfort (Carol Stream, Il: Tyndale House Publishers, 2006), 343.

LOVELIFE

BIBLIOGRAPHY

BIBLIOGRAPHY

Alexander, David and Pat, ed. *Eerdman's Handbook to the Bible*. Grand Rapids: William B. Eerdman's Publishing Company, 1983.

Dyer, Charles, and Eugene Merrill. *Nelson's Old Testament Survey*. Nashville: Thomas Nelson, 2001.

Geisler, Norman, and Thomas Howe. *When Critics Ask: A Popular Handbook on Bible Difficulties*. Grand Rapids: Baker Books, 1999.

Kinlaw, Dennis F. "Song of Songs." In *The Expositor's Bible Commentary*, ed. Frank E. Gaebelein, vol. 5. 12 vols. Grand Rapids: Zondervan, 1991.

Longman III, Tremper. *Song of Songs*. Vol. 6. 18 vols. Cornerstone Biblical Commentary, ed. Philip W. Comfort. Carol Stream, Il: Tyndale House Publishers, 2006.

Longman, Tremper III and Raymond B. Dillard. *An Introduction to the Old Testament*. Grand Rapids: Zondervan, 2006.

MacDonald, WIlliam. *Believer's Bible Commentary*. Edited by Art Farstad. Nashville: Thomas Nelson Publishers, 1995.

Provan, Iain. *The NIV Application Commentary*, Ecclesiastes/Song of Songs. Grand Rapids: Zondervan, 2001.

Radmacher, Earl, Ronald B. Allen, and H. Wayne House, ed. *Nelson's New Illustrated Bible Commentary*. Nashville: Nelson, 1999.

Wiersbe, Warren. *The Bible Exposition Commentary: Old Testament Wisdom and History*. Colorado Springs: Victor, 2003.

LOVELIFE

APPENDIX

appeNdix

TEXT ANSWERS - SESSION ONE

Question One
1. pleasure
2. children
3. oneness
4. comfort
5. protection
6. to glorify God

TEXT ANSWERS - SESSION FOUR

Question Three
1. Quality Time
2. Service
3. Gifts
4. Touch
5. Words of Affirmation

LOVELIFE

ICE BREAKERS

ICEBreakers

SESSION ONE:
Group members write one unexpected fact about themselves on an index card. Shuffle, read each card to the group, have the group vote for who they think the card belongs to. [Variation: Each person writes 3 unexpected facts—one of them is false. Group chooses what they think is NOT true.]

SESSION TWO:
What first attracted you to your spouse?

SESSION THREE:
Describe your bedroom in one phrase. (For example, "the junk drawer gone wild," "my office away from the office," "the TV room," "En-Gedi.") On a scale of 1-10 how happy are you with it?

SESSION FOUR:
What is your "pet peeve"?

SESSION FIVE:
Ask group members to bring their wedding albums to show the group. Share a memorable event from your wedding.]

SESSION SIX:
Group members write one unexpected fact about themselves on an index card. Shuffle, read each card to the group, have the group vote for who they think the card belongs to. [Variation: Each person writes 3 unexpected facts—one of them is false. Group chooses what they think is NOT true.]

SESSION SEVEN:
What animal best represents your personality? (If you were involved in a conflict, would you pick a different animal?)

SESSION EIGHT:
If you had all day to do whatever you want, what would you do?

SESSION NINE:
Describe the most generous gift you have ever received. What quality made it special?

SESSION TEN:
Split into two groups—guys and gals. What is one question you would like to ask the opposite sex? Take some time to have the ladies answer questions from the men and vice versa. *Some sample questions:*

- What are ways that we (men) can affirm you (ladies) in public?
- What are the most frustrating things about our gender?
- What are the best differences between men and women that helps a marriage thrive?

NOTES

LOVELIFE

response card

- ◯ I am single and committed to pray for God's best in my romantic life.
- ◯ I am married and commit to apply the principles I've learned to my marriage.
- ◯ I prayed to receive Christ as my Lord and Savior today.
- ◯ I am interested in finding out more about a personal relationship with Jesus Christ.
- ◯ _____
  _____

Church you attend _____

connecting

If you would like to learn more about **Pastor Mark** and the ministries he is involved with or access all of sermons online, please visit these websites:

www.marshillchurch.org

www.theresurgence.com

www.acts29network.org

response card

Name _____

Address _____

City _____ State_____ Zip _____

Phone (_____) _____

Email _____

Comments about the **LoveLife Conference**:

_____

_____

_____

○ I give permission for my comments to be used by the **LoveLife Conference**.

How did you hear about the **LoveLife Conference**:

○ Church _____

○ Radio Station _____   ○ Newspaper/Magazine   ○ Friend

○ Other _____

THE  HUB   n e w   r e s o u r c e !

PHILIPPIANS
To Live is Christ & to Die is Gain

Find contentment in life. Even in pain. If you are looking for your next small group study, then look no further.

Join **Matt Chandler**, Pastor of *The Village Church*, and walk through this study on joy, contentment, and purpose, no matter the circumstances.

Now you can buy the DVD set, or buy/rent each session online. **www.gotothehub.com**